THE
WRITER'S
PROCESS

WORKBOOK

Also by Anne Janzer

The Writer's Process: Getting Your Brain in Gear

The Workplace Writer's Process:
A Guide to Getting the Job Done

Writing to Be Understood:
What Works and Why

Get the Word Out:
Write a Book That Makes a Difference

33 Ways Not to Screw Up Your Business Emails

Subscription Marketing:
Strategies for Nurturing Customers
in a World of Churn

THE
WRITER'S
PROCESS

WORKBOOK

SIMPLE PRACTICES FOR FINDING
YOUR BEST PROCESS

ANNE JANZER

Cuesta Park Consulting

Cuesta Park Consulting

San Luis Obispo, California
Copyright © 2022 by Anne Janzer

Printed in the United States of America

ISBN: 978-1-952284-08-3

Contents

PART FOUR
Find Flow **55**

PART FIVE
Your Writing Recipe **73**

Introduction

When I first wrote *The Writer's Process: Getting Your Brain in Gear*, I hoped it would help other writers with their work. But the magnitude of the response surprised me.

Countless people have told me that the book unblocked writing projects or validated their practices. Writers tend to worry about being crazy or unusual, and it's reassuring to realize that we share the same issues.

The Muse and the Scribe metaphors gave many writers fresh insight into why they have drawers full of unfinished projects and what to do about it. Others seized on the bread-baking analogy and developed their own recipes. People have described the book's impact in emails, blog and social media posts, podcast conversations, and in one memorable case, a college writing assignment forwarded by the professor.

Those responses motivated me to create this workbook. Because it's one thing to read a book and quite another to dislodge existing thought patterns, establish new writing habits, and build skills. Changing your patterns requires action—and writing.

Finding *Your* Process

My writing process evolved over years of freelance content creation in the business world. Being paid for each completed project strengthened my inner writing discipline (my Scribe). But my creative processes languished until I learned how to actively invite my Muse to the work. That changed everything.

Eventually I came up with a writing recipe that consistently delivers the best results in the shortest time. Then came the hard part—learning to trust that process.

Of course, my process won't look just like yours. No one can tell you exactly how to write.

Perhaps you're strongly creative but need help finishing the work. Or you struggle to find time for writing in your life or keep getting distracted before you finish anything.

Use this workbook as an opportunity explore what works best for you. Once you've completed it, you should know how to protect and defend your writing practices in the rush of an impatient and distraction-filled world.

How to Use This Book

This workbook is a companion to *The Writer's Process*. If you haven't read the book, don't worry. You'll find explanations of key concepts as you go.

The practices here include ideas directly from *The Writer's Process*, as well as exercises that I've developed for myself and to help other writers.

They're not all original—people have been writing and teaching writing for centuries. Many will look familiar, and you won't need or want to use all of them.

Your personal assessment of your Muse and Scribe (see Part One) should help you understand which practices you need to adopt and why. You can zip right past the others guilt-free.

Some of the exercises are one-time activities designed to deliver insight into your own patterns. Experiment with the forms, checklists, and journaling activities to embed new practices into your writing life. You might return to a few of them later if you hit a bump in your writing road.

Fill in the forms in this book or download them from my website. If you see the pencil icon ✏️▷, the form is available at AnneJanzer.com/Resources. Or simply create your own and write in a journal.

No matter how you use it, I hope that this book gives you more faith, joy, and mastery in your personal writing process.

Let's find the writing recipe that works best for you.

PART ONE

THE MUSE AND THE SCRIBE

Writing isn't a single act. It's a compound, multistep process that engages various parts of our brain in multiple types of attention and thought.

To simplify our approach to writing, let's adopt a useful fiction. Let's imagine that we have within us two distinct writing systems, characterized by the personas of the *Muse* and the *Scribe*. The Muse is responsible for creativity and the Scribe for disciplined productivity.

Most of us associate more with one or the other. Successful writing requires a balance of the two. Often, the Muse and Scribe collaborate. Both are essential to successful writing.

In this section, you'll take a closer look at your own inner Muse and Scribe.

1

Defining the Muse

Creative insight springs from the Muse.

Writers like to think of the Muse as something outside of their direct control. (If you've ever been part of a team "brainstorming" session, you know how hard it is to force creativity on demand.) The Greeks worshipped the Muses as gods. Many writers do the same.

However you picture your Muse, it's part of who you are, rather than a mystical entity from beyond. Your Muse lives in the following thought processes and activities:

- Associative thinking
- Intuition
- Empathy
- Brainstorming
- Contemplation/mind wandering

We cannot force creative insights to happen, but we can invite the Muse into our lives. Part Two, Welcome the Muse, offers a range of ideas for enticing the Muse into your writing life.

First, take a good look at your own Muse.

How Does Your Muse Show Up?

Take a moment to think about the role of the Muse in your writing life. If you write in different formats and genres (reports at work, poetry at home), think about one specific type of writing that's important to you.

Which of the following best characterizes your personal Muse?

Shy Muse

You may think of yourself as "not a creative type." Coming up with new ideas is difficult, and you'd rather work with other people's assignments. Your Muse may be shy and withdrawing. Perhaps, in the past, you've had ideas and shot them down quickly. This has trained your Muse to keep quiet.

Temperamental Muse

Good ideas sometimes come out of nowhere, but rarely when you need them. It feels entirely out of your control. Your Muse is fickle and unreliable. (This is a normal part of the human condition, by the way.)

Reliable Muse

You have some confidence in your ability to generate ideas when needed. They may not come easily. You wish that they would arrive on cue. But you've got a reasonable handle on your creative processes and come up with enough ideas to get the job done.

Prolific Muse

People come to you because they know that you're a creative person. You have plenty of ideas for projects—perhaps even too many! Sometimes, however, the constant flood of inspiration gets in the way of accomplishing anything. You're easily distracted by the next project.

My Muse

Where do you fall on this scale? Assess your Muse for all of the types of writing that you do.

- ☑ Shy Muse
- ☐ Temperamental Muse
- ☐ Reliable Muse
- ☐ Prolific Muse

If your Muse shows up differently for different types of writing, make a note of that here. (For example, Shy Muse for business writing, Prolific Muse for fiction.)

_____

_____

_____

_____

Now that you've got a handle on your Muse, let's move on to the inner Scribe.

2

Defining the Scribe

The Scribe embodies the productive self. It handles everything from getting your butt in the chair or pen on paper to releasing your finished works to the world. (Yes, the Scribe handles publication.)

The Scribe controls these inner processes:

- Linear, analytical thinking
- Research and organization
- Critical judgment
- Self-discipline
- Project management
- Focused attention

As writers, we tend to worship the Muse and undervalue the Scribe's grubbier, more mundane tasks. But without a fully functioning Scribe, your words will never reach the larger world. If you want to communicate with others through your writing, you need a stable and reliable Scribe.

How Does Your Scribe Take Charge?

As you did with the Muse, think about how the Scribe fits into your writing life. Which of the following best describes your writing discipline?

Slacker Scribe

Maybe you can't find the time to write. Or you work only when you're inspired or love the project. That means you wait for inspiration. Deadlines have little power over you. You rarely complete things to the standard that you want to achieve. We've all spent time with a Slacker Scribe, so there's no shame here. But if you want to publish your writing, strengthen your Scribe.

Distracted Scribe

Perhaps you start out strong on a writing project, then can't maintain the pace or find that life gets in the way. You may feel like you end the day farther behind than you started. Life challenges all of us with competing priorities. But when your Scribe is easily distracted, you find it difficult to finish writing projects.

Reliable Scribe

You have a good handle on how to get projects done. You meet most of your deadlines and obligations. Sometimes, of course, you falter, or you are not as productive as you might like. It's not always pretty or easy. But when you need to do it, you get the work done.

Scrupulous Scribe

You never miss a deadline and are meticulous about meeting commitments. You stick to schedules without deviation. You have a reputation for getting remarkable things done, and people often call on you because of it. Your meticulousness can be a curse if it crowds out creativity and inspiration. You can easily exhaust yourself.

My Scribe

Where does your Scribe fall in these categories?

- ☐ Slacker Scribe
- ☐ Distracted Scribe
- ☐ Reliable Scribe
- ☐ Scrupulous Scribe

If your Scribe shows up differently for different types of writing, make a note of it here. (For example, Scrupulous Scribe for business writing, Slacker Scribe for poetry.)

_____

_____

_____

_____

3

Assess Your Balance

Successful writing requires contributions from both the Muse and the Scribe in the *right balance* for the projects you're working on.

All good writing requires contributions from the Muse, but the amount varies. Fiction writers need input from the Muse for plot ideas and a Reliable Scribe to turn ideas into published books. Many nonfiction writers rely more heavily on the Scribe yet need the Muse's gifts to create something worth reading.

So, how's *your* Muse/Scribe balance? Look at your personal self-assessment and think about how well the balance matches the work you do. Given the needs of your genre, is your Muse too weak? Does the Scribe run the show too much?

- ☐ My Muse is stronger than my Scribe
- ☐ My Scribe overpowers my Muse
- ☐ They take turns running the show
- ☐ They manage to work together

Balance matters. A Scrupulous Scribe can be too much of a good thing unless it's matched by a Reliable Muse. You may spend your time working diligently on projects that don't inspire you, leaving messy creativity at the door.

Similarly, a Prolific Muse can overwhelm a Distracted Scribe, leading you from one project to another without completing any of them.

We have natural strengths and weaknesses, and many of us find ourselves out of balance on occasion—especially when we attempt a new kind of writing.

Use the insights of the previous pages to place yourself on the Writing Quadrant. (If quadrants don't make sense, skip straight to the descriptions below and see which ones match your experience.)

- The x axis represents the Scribe—the stronger your Scribe, the farther to the right you put yourself in the quadrant.
- The y axis represents the Muse —the stronger your Muse, the higher you travel in the quadrant.

This gives us four general areas of writing balance:

1. Creative Productivity
2. Uninspired Inertia
3. Creative Chaos
4. Diligent Drudgery

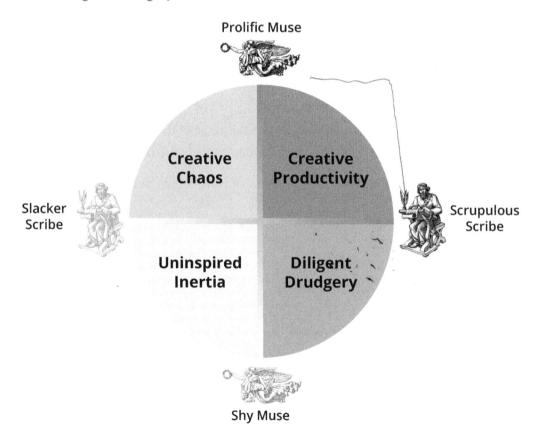

Creative Productivity

In the top right area, the Muse and Scribe both contribute to the writing. When you're in this mode:

- You feel confident that you can deliver a writing assignment or make a meaningful contribution to a project.
- When you're engaged in the work, the writing comes relatively easily.

If you want to be a professional writer, spend as much time as you can in this quadrant or you'll burn out quickly. Even if you're there most of the time, life can throw you out of balance for a while.

Uninspired Inertia

With a Slacker Scribe and Shy Muse, you sit around and think about writing rather than doing it. You may hear thoughts like this going through your head:

I want to write something, but I'm waiting for inspiration. Once I come up with a great idea, I'll start writing.

Inspiration doesn't usually come to those who wait. It comes to those who work. If you find yourself in this area, learn how to activate both your Muse and your Scribe in the following sections.

Creative Chaos

Are you a prolific idea person? When your Muse overwhelms the Scribe, you may not get where you want to be. For example:

- You love starting stories, but endings remain unwritten.
- You have notebooks filled with ideas but can't seem to find the time to turn any of them into completed work.
- You switch between projects without completing them.

If this sounds familiar, don't worry. You simply need to prod your Scribe into action. See the exercises in Part Three: Strengthen the Scribe.

Diligent Drudgery

What happens when you have plenty of discipline and work ethic, but lack creative inspiration? When the Scribe overpowers the Muse, you can finish the writing but the process isn't fun.

When you're in a state of Diligent Drudgery, you might think:

I'm great at editing and revising other people's work but can't come up with my own creative works.
Writing this thing feels like pulling teeth—why is it so hard?

The Muse makes the writing process better, faster, and more fun. Turn to the exercises on strengthening the Muse in Part Two.

Where Do You Spend Your Writing Time?

Look at your personal Muse/Scribe balance and decide where you spend most of your time.

Use the following list to order them—1 for the most time, 4 for the least:

__2__ Creative Productivity
__1__ Creative Chaos
__3__ Diligent Drudgery
__4__ Uninspired Inertia

Describe how the balance changes for the type of writing you do:

I'm always at creative chaos, but Creative P. and Diligent Drudgery come in heavy. Making my process overwhelming, complex and stressful.

If you need to move to the Creative Productivity region, learn how to strengthen the Muse or the Scribe in Parts Two and Three.

PART TWO

WELCOME THE MUSE

The Muse embodies the creative, intuitive processes that help you find the perfect analogy, a fascinating story, or an unusual approach to your topic. If you want more creativity in your writing or your life, start by understanding what the Muse feels like when it is present. Learn what thoughts, activities, or mindsets attract the Muse when it does show up. Then learn to spend more time engaging in them.

The first few exercises in this section help you recognize and welcome the Muse into your life.

Of course, the Muse doesn't always appear even when you create the right conditions. You need to lure it into your life. The second part of this section includes exercises for actively enticing the Muse to show up.

4

Notice When the Muse Is Present

Inspiration doesn't always arrive with a blinding flash or a big "Aha!" moment. Sometime the Muse whispers quietly in your ear. Those ideas waver at the edge of your consciousness. Your Muse might be shy or easily spooked by the presence of other people, urgent tasks, and the rush of the day.

The first step in welcoming the Muse is simply *noticing* when it wants to contribute. Pay attention to situations that attract your Muse.

Places
Where are you when inspiration shows up? (At your desk, in the shower, on a walk?) List as many of those places as you can.

Before Trying to sleep, listening to music, reading, movie theater, shower, car rides

Alone or with Others?
Are you alone? With one or two close friends or colleagues? Surrounded by strangers in a coffee shop? Does it matter?

Both. Doesn't matter for me.

Time of Day

Chronobiology suggests that biological creatures follow different rhythms and timings.

Are you more creative first thing in the morning? Last thing at night? When you wake up at 5 a.m. and don't want to get out of bed yet? What times are especially fertile for you?

Late at night usually.

Other Observations

Have you noticed any other trends about your personal creativity?

Usually daily but can be sporadic. They come at any time. Some stay in my head for a while. I come back to them mentally but don't always dive into them. Others work helps but not all the time. It made things complicated a lot.

If you're not sure of these answers, spend a few days paying attention to the quiet voice of the Muse as it shows up with unexpected associations or interesting ideas to explore.

◆

Noticing Your Muse: A Journal

Every time you have an unexpected insight, an urge to write, an interesting idea, or a particularly creative and productive writing session, make a note of the situation.

Keep a notebook or phone by your side to jot down ideas when they arrive, as well as what you were doing at the time. Then enter them in this journal and look for patterns.

Try this for a few days, a week, or however long it takes to accumulate a number of entries. Notice how often the Muse gets your attention, how strongly, and what you're doing.

As a bonus, you might discover that you've been ignoring creative insights!

Here are the prompts for your journal:

Idea:

Where I was:

When it was:

What I was doing:

Who was with me:

Muse Journal

DATE	IDEA	OBSERVATIONS
4/8/23	Government Picks a serial killer out of the babies born that year. The unknowing victim then	Where I was: Bedroom When: Daytime What I was doing: Talking Who was around me: Mus
4/10/23	Serial killer among the people that are supposed to search for him	Where: Bedroom When: Nighttime What: Writing here Who: Mus
		Where: When: What: Who:
		Where: When: What: Who:
		Where: When: What: Who:
		Where: When: What: Who:

5

Identify Open Attention

Have ideas ever popped into your head while you are doing any of the following?

- ☑ Taking a shower
- ☑ Exercising
- ☑ Walking outdoors
- ☐ Playing with the dog
- ☑ Doing housework like ironing, dishes, or vacuuming
- ☑ Driving on a familiar route or commuting to/from work

Those activities each require *partial* attention, leaving brain cycles free to wander. Instead of focused attention, they are periods of *open attention*.

The Muse is associated with nonlinear, associative thought. When you focus attention on a pressing problem, you may not notice the quiet contributions of the Muse.

No matter how busy you are, you probably have windows of open attention in your life. Writers know to protect and expand that time.

Return to the previous exercise of noticing when the Muse was present. Would you categorize those episodes as open attention? What other times do you have in your day that might be ripe for inviting the Muse?

Identify three periods of open attention in your ordinary schedule.

My Top Three Open Attention Activities

1. _Anytime I'm trying to do something else_
2. _Trying to relax or nap_
3. _Bedtime Routine_

If you don't have a top three, or if you want even more, you may have to clear away activities otherwise occupying your open attention. That's the next practice.

6

Make Time for Open Attention

Periods of open attention don't look "productive" in the eyes of the world. So, to accomplish more, we multitask, streaming podcasts while driving, making phone calls on our walks, and listening to audiobooks while doing housework.

Protect the open attention in your life. Schedule it if you must.

Use the weekly schedule on the next page and mark every reliable opportunity for open attention. Make a quick time estimate for each.

For example:

Monday:
Doing dishes: 10 minutes
Driving to/from work: 40 minutes
Workout: 30 minutes
Total: 80 minutes

Then see what it adds up to.

Open Attention Estimates

DAY	OPEN ATTENTION PERIODS	TOTAL
Monday		
Tuesday		
Wednesday		
Thursday		
Friday		
Saturday		
Sunday		
Total available time in the week:		

Scope Out the Competition

Are you surprised by the weekly total on the previous page?

Chances are, you have a healthy amount of *potential* open attention time. If you're like most of us, you fill it with other things.

Identify your top open attention fillers. Here are a few popular ones—do they apply to you?

- ☐ Checking social media
- ☐ Listening to podcasts or audiobooks
- ☐ Talking on the phone
- ☐ Texting friends
- ☑ Reading/watching the news
- ☐ Watching the TV in the gym when you work out

My top three open attention fillers:

1. _Youtube_
2. _Pinterest_
3. _Reading (Mangas, Novels, etc)_

You don't have ~~to stop~~ doing these activities. Instead, prioritize open attention. Use the other things you enjoy as an incentive. For example, if you have a 30-minute commute, let your mind wander the first 15 minutes, then listen to an audiobook for the last 15 minutes.

I resolve to make more time for creativity by...

Engaging in more activities that give me the chance to have open attention

7

Add a Gentle Nudge

Simply making time for open attention may be enough to attract the Muse. You go for that walk, or take a drive, and then the Muse starts showing up with ideas and suggestions.

However, your mind might wander off in many directions. The Muse is easily distracted and may be much more interested in thinking about the plot of that television series or ruminating on a perceived slight at work than contributing to your writing.

In these situations, adopt the gentle nudge.

Here's how it works.

Create an inspiration to-do list.
Identify one or two things you want to invite the Muse to work on in the background. For example:

- A fresher metaphor to replace overly used ones (like sports and warfare metaphors in business)
- The topic of your next blog post
- Your main character's favorite food
- Rhyming word combinations

Keep the list short. One or two items is enough for any given day.

Remind yourself.

Recall the list when you're in a period of open attention. Think about it gently. Remember, you're not focusing specifically on anything.

Invite your brain to ponder the problem. Of course it will wander off, that's normal. When you notice, remind yourself of the topic in a friendly and positive way. "Oh yes, I wonder what I should write about in that blog post…"

This practice trains your Muse to show up and contribute.

Capture the contributions.

If ideas arise, write them down! Don't let the inner critic tear them apart before they see the light of day. A so-so idea, if acknowledged and recorded, can lead you to a better one.

Try it and see if it works for you.

My Inspiration To-Do List

The life of my characters
Horror close to humanity
Topics of poetry
Writing help

Results of Nudging

Did the gentle nudge work for you? Make a note of the ideas you came up with and what it felt like.

- Torm/Fanx fit well into each other's lives though they are a mystery to the other
- Want to delve into the lines between life and death. Are the clinically dead "aware" when they are brought "back"
- My struggles with suicidal thoughts, grief, and the unknown of tomorrow
- Find simple writing examples

8

Summary and Commitments for Your Muse

Remember these key points about welcoming and empowering your Muse.

- Notice when the Muse contributes. Pay attention to where you are and what you're doing.
- Protect periods of open attention in your daily life.
- Write down and honor the contributions of the Muse, even if your rational mind tells you that they're not so hot.
- Make a "creativity to-do" list and revisit its contents when you're in open attention.

My Top Open Attention Activities

1. _____

2. _____

3. _____

Commitments to My Muse

What will you do differently in your life to make the Muse feel welcome? How will you honor its contributions?

_____

_____

_____

_____

PART THREE

STRENGTHEN THE SCRIBE

The Scribe manages the productive part of your writing process. It meets deadlines, organizes research, and generally gets things done.

The exercises in this section will help you strengthen the Scribe overall. When you have a specific project you need to complete, refer to the ideas in the following pages for adding urgency and accountability.

Even as you work on your Scribe, make sure to practice self-compassion. Find ideas for adding self-care to your writing life as well.

Let's get your Scribe in gear!

9

Daily Practice

Nearly every writer and writing coach repeats a variation on this advice: Write every day. Every single day.

That's great advice. But just between you and me, it's not the *only* path to getting work out into the world. You don't have to work on your book or blog posts or poems every day. (Don't tell anyone I said this or I'll be banned from writer's conferences.)

Some people finish books by working in three long blocks of time a week. (You can *bet* that their Muses work in the background around the clock.) As a nonfiction author, I am often researching or planning rather than writing manuscripts.

Yet, I still write every day in a journal because this habit trains *both* the Muse and the Scribe.

The Muse: Daily appearances with a pen or keyboard in hand convince the Muse that you're serious about this writing thing, and it will start looking for connections and ideas when you're not actively writing.

The Scribe: When you commit to a daily writing practice, the Scribe must prioritize writing over other activities. Like regular exercise, the benefits accrue over time.

Create a writing practice that makes sense for your life and work.

Minimum Daily Writing Requirement

Define the minimum that you'll do, measured by length or time. For example:

- 5 minutes
- 200 words online
- One page in a paper journal

Rather than setting an ambitious daily goal, start small. It's easier to commit to a new habit when you only have to find five minutes. You can always do more, but try to show up and do at least the minimum.

Five minutes might not generate a lot of writing, but it does reinforce your sense of identity as a person who writes every day—a real writer. And often, once you get started you keep going.

A Daily Project

What kind of writing will you do in this time? What counts as meeting this writing obligation? My advice: Give yourself permission to work on a wide range of projects in your minimum daily writing requirement.

Here are a few examples.

- A journal collecting a specific type of writing, such as observations from nature, recollections from the past, or stories
- "Morning pages" journals exploring creative thoughts or mining your recent experiences and emotions. (See Julia Cameron's *The Artist's Way* for a description of morning pages.)
- Letters or online correspondence to loved ones (*not* business emails)
- A work in progress like a novel or book manuscript
- Posts for a blog

This daily writing habit isn't necessarily about cranking out more work. No one needs to see what you're writing. The work may generate fodder for your other, public-facing writing, or provide new paths to explore.

This is about process, not outcomes.

Once you establish the writing habit, you might easily rotate between types or projects. For example, for a month or so, collect stories in a journal. If you're ready to start writing a manuscript, make that the daily project.

When the manuscript goes into production, choose another focus for your daily writing, perhaps a journal of the process and your feelings.

Set your commitment below, then track it. Keeping a record can help you stay on track. It's a visual reminder of progress, and it's satisfying to add the day's entry.

Use the Writing Record sheet that follows or download tracking sheets from the Resources page on AnneJanzer.com.

Daily Writing Commitment

I commit to the following daily writing goal (pick one and enter the minimum goal):

☐ Words:

☐ Minutes:

☐ Pages:

In this time, I will work on the following project(s):

_____

_____

Daily Writing Record

DAY/TIME	WORDS WRITTEN/TIME SPENT	OBSERVATIONS

10

Find the Time

A while ago, I surveyed more than 400 nonfiction authors about their processes and results. In response to the question about where (if anywhere) they got stuck, the most common answer was "finding the time to write."

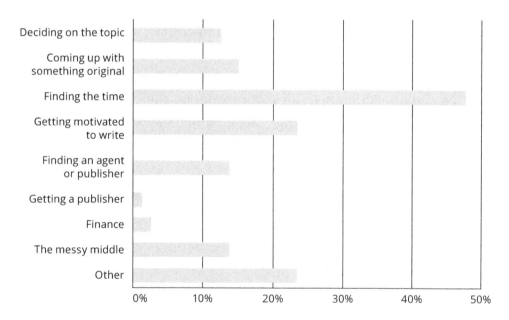

Question: If you're stuck, what's getting in the way?

If you struggle with finding time, you are not alone.

We all have the same number of hours and minutes in the day. Yet we face varying demands on our time. Perhaps you juggle multiple high-priority items. You might be moving, or caring for someone who is acutely ill—we may have little control over those events.

Too often, though, we neglect the time we have. When we say we don't have enough time, we really mean that writing isn't a high enough priority.

Before you can find time, look at how you're spending it. Do an audit.

Audit Your Time

Take a look at your day, hour by hour, from waking in the morning to going to bed at night. I've included a sample journal that you can copy and use. But there are many ways to do an audit:

- Use a calendar or daily journal.
- Find online software. You can download a free schedule maker from Nir Eyal: Nirandfar.com/timeboxing.

Run the audit for a week, or at least a few days.

Keep the calendar or paper handy as you go about your day. Or check in a few times each day, perhaps at meals and bedtime, and fill it in as best you can.

Identify what you do in blocks of 30 minutes or more, to the best of your recollection. Group similar activities. For example, showering and dressing and breakfast could be an hourlong "Morning necessity" block. If you're at work for a certain number of hours a day, you can block that time out as "work."

If you can't remember what you did in a time period, make a note of that, too. Put a question mark there. That's an interesting opportunity to look for time that you might free up for writing.

Time Audit Sheet

Use a calendar, a time tracking app, or the worksheet below.

	MONDAY	TUESDAY	WEDNESDAY	THURSDAY	FRIDAY	SATURDAY	SUNDAY
7:00							
8:00							
9:00							
10:00							
11:00							
12:00							
1:00							
2:00							
3:00							
4:00							
5:00							
6:00							
7:00							
8:00							
9:00							
10:00							
11:00							

Analyze the Results

Have you completed the audit? Look at what you've entered and categorize your activities. Use highlighters and color codes if that works for you. Mark the following:

- Unavoidable (you've got to eat, get enough sleep, shower)
- Important (spending time with your spouse or family, self-care, paid work, writing)
- Urgent (fixing the car, paying taxes)

Where does writing fit into this schedule? If writing isn't in the Important category, it won't get done.

Can you spot activities that you might be able to "borrow time" from for the writing? Any activities without categories?

Important mindset note: Approach this project with curiosity, not self-judgment. None of us spend our time on a treadmill of perfect productivity. We're human. Don't beat yourself up.

Leave time for self-care. Exercise, sleep, time with family, reading a good book—these are activities that energize you. But be careful what you put into this bucket. There's a difference between intentionally watching your favorite show in the evening (which might be self-care or a treat) and mindlessly getting lost in the rabbit hole of social media or browsing YouTube.

Don't *stop* doing the fun things, but do them intentionally, as a form of self-care. You'll enjoy them more if you have made time for important work, like writing, first.

11

Put Important Things First

Perhaps you cannot find anything to eliminate from your schedule. Fair enough. But many tasks are like sponges—they'll soak up all the space available to them.

Try this: Reorder your work so that you do the writing first.

I'm not a morning person. But like many writers, I choose to write before I dive into the day's urgencies. Email, social media, the news: these activities claim our attention and focus, crowding out the quiet contributions of the Muse.

Writing for even a few minutes before you jump into the fast-rushing stream of the day can make a difference. Plus, you'll feel that satisfaction of knowing that you have done at least some of your important writing, no matter what else the day throws at you.

Try this: Use writing as a precondition for checking your email and social media. Don't check them until you've sat down with your manuscript, journal, or daily writing practice.

You can use a journal to help you focus on the important tasks.

The Daily "Important Things" Journal

If writing is new to your life, it may need to earn its priority in your schedule.

Use journaling to remind yourself that it's important to you.

Start a journal or written record. Every morning, ask yourself explicitly, "What are the most important things I need to do today?"

Don't pick more than three. Make sure that most days, writing is one of the three.

In the evening, check in again and review how you did.

This simple task focuses the mind. It also helps you understand what might be pulling you from your course.

(John Steinbeck did this morning/evening check-in in his journal while writing his novels. He started plenty of mornings late after staying up drinking, though, so let's not emulate that part.)

Put Important Things First

DAY	TASKS	RESULTS/OBSERVATIONS
Monday	1. 2. 3.	
Tuesday	1. 2. 3.	
Wednesday	1. 2. 3.	
Thursday	1. 2. 3.	
Friday	1. 2. 3.	
Saturday	1. 2. 3.	
Sunday	1. 2. 3.	

12

Make It Urgent with Deadlines

"There is an insidious tendency to neglect important tasks
that do not have to be done today—or even this week."
– Charles E. Hummel, *Tyranny of the Urgent*

If maintaining an Important Things journal doesn't help, then maybe being *important* is not enough. Maybe your writing needs *urgency* as well.

That's where deadlines come in. When we write for our own projects, we often lack external deadlines. And without a deadline, urgent tasks creep in front of the writing—even if they are less important.

Well-constructed deadlines give your writing achievable but powerful urgency. They motivate the Scribe, giving it a reason to show up and insist on action.

However, deadlines don't work for everyone. A little self-knowledge comes in handy.

How Conscientious Are You?

How do you do with deadlines? In school, did you turn in projects on time, or were you always begging for extensions? Do you have a Reliable Scribe or a Slacker Scribe?

Conscientiousness is one of the "big five" personality factors cited by psychologists who try to define personality. If you are highly conscientious, you are diligent about meeting your obligations.

Of course, you may be conscientious about one area of your life, and less so in another. Plus, our personality attributes can change over time.

How conscientious are you currently about your writing?

☐ Not very. I just can't make myself write yet.
☐ Somewhat. I work consistently for a while, then stop.
☐ Moderately. I write regularly, but not as much as I hope.
☐ Strongly. Once I commit to a project, I do it.

If you are somewhat conscientious, deploy deadlines to put that personality trait to work in your writing.

If you don't have external deadlines, make your own. Make sure that they are reasonable and achievable, but near enough on the calendar to keep you moving.

Here are two approaches to creating deadlines for your writing: top-down and bottom-up.

Different projects may work better with one of these strategies. You may also find it useful to try both approaches and then reconcile them. The bottom-up deadlines will help you understand where you might be short-changing individual steps.

Top-Down Deadlines

Start with the final product—an article, a blog post, a short story, a poem, a book.

When do you realistically want to finish it, based on the time available and the amount of work involved? Make that date your deadline.

Now identify interim deadlines or milestones. These may include:

• Interviewing three people
• Creating a tentative outline
• Finishing a specific chapter

Break long projects, like books, into smaller chunks, like chapters, phases of the work, or sections. Figure out how long each of these steps should take, and work backward from your final deadline to create interim dates.

Here's a simple example:

TASK	DURATION	START BY DATE	END BY DATE
Formatting and proofreading	5 days	June 27	**Final Deadline: July 1**
Copyediting	1 week	June 20	June 27
Revising	2 weeks	June 6	June 20
Rough Draft	3 weeks	May 16	June 6
Outline	1 week	May 9	May 16
Research	10 days	April 30	May 9

Use the planning guide on the next page or create your own. Post your schedule where you can see it. Remind the Scribe that it has important work to do.

If you miss a deadline, rework the plan and re-post it.

Top-Down Planning Guide

TASK	DURATION	START BY DATE	END BY DATE
			Deadline

Bottom-Up Deadlines

If top-down planning seems overwhelming or you're not sure where to start, try setting bottom-up deadlines.

This planning approach operates on the philosophy that we accomplish important work by just doing the next step and having faith in the process.

To create a bottom-up plan, identify the first small step in the project. Nothing major. Instead of *Research my book*, write *Research what people ate in Revolutionary Boston*.

Write it down. Give yourself a deadline for that small step. Decide how long it will take and pick the next step.

Continue sketching these things out, assigning time, and stringing them together.

See where you end up with a final deadline as a result. If you breeze through early steps, you will reach the finish faster.

Bottom-Up Planning Sheet

This is simply the inverse of the top-down planning sheet.

TASK	DURATION	START BY DATE	END BY DATE
			Deadline

13

Add Accountability

"I love deadlines. I like the whooshing sound
they make as they fly by."
– Douglas Adams

When you write for yourself, nobody hovers over your shoulder asking to see your copy. Even if you have a book deal, the deadline is usually far away—until suddenly it's not.

With no one watching, it's easy to toss in the towel and do something else when the writing gets tough. Many people need *external* motivation or accountability to power through to the finish.

Give your Scribe the strength to withstand the temptations of the world by adding accountability to others.

Find an Accountability Partner

Find another writer who wants an accountability partner. Then agree on what you'll hold each other accountable for.

For example, you might tell your partner that you're going to write every day. You might arrange to check in via text every evening to report if you're done. Or you might agree to report on your progress on a story every Monday night.

You, in turn, can provide the accountability the partner needs. Put it in your schedule and take care of it.

Join a Writer's Group

If you're not comfortable seeking out an individual accountability partner, consider joining a writing or critique group.

Many communities have writing groups where you can submit a few pages for critiquing on a monthly or weekly basis. The quality of the critique will vary according to the participants and how well they match your readers.

For some authors, the real value of the critique group is the sense of accountability it creates. Knowing that someone is going to read and discuss your work with you should motivate you to get it done.

Reward Yourself

What motivates you? Give yourself a reward when you meet a significant deadline. (It's always good to celebrate how far you've come.)

Raise the Stakes

In his book *Indistractable*, Nir Eyal suggests that you give a reasonable sum of money to a friend to hold you accountable for completing your task. If you fail, your friend agrees to donate money to a cause you *really* disagree with. (For me, this might be the Society to Abolish Chocolate.)

This adds real pain to missing a deadline. In addition to losing the money, your lack of commitment ends up supporting a cause you detest.

That's an extreme measure. But if that's what it takes, give it a try.

Your Accountability Plan

Who will hold you accountable?

_____

_____

How often will you check in?

_____

_____

Do you need extra incentives? If so, what will you choose?

- ☐ Reward
- ☐ Penalty for not making it

Name the reward/penalty

_____

_____

14

Practice Self-Compassion

Before we leave this section, remember to practice self-compassion. Yes, high standards and deadlines are important. But taken to extremes, they can become impossible masters.

Aggressive goals and rigid systems may work in the short term but are bound to either fail or soften in the long term. You're crafting a writing life, so find a sustainable pace.

It's more important for your long-term health as a writer to show yourself compassion.

If your Scribe is still distracted after doing the exercises here, be kind. If you were mentoring another writer, what advice would you give them in a similar situation?

Would you berate them for being lazy, distracted, or not prioritizing appropriately? Or would you be compassionate, gentle, and firmly encouraging, hoping to help them back on track?

I hope, as a mentor, you'd choose compassion. Give yourself the same grace.

Be Kind to Yourself

If you've been driving yourself hard or if life has been piling on, revisit activities that replenish your energy. Here are a few things to consider:

- ☐ Taking time to rest
- ☐ Reading a beloved book
- ☐ Getting out in nature
- ☐ Spending time with supportive friends or family
- ☐ Baking
- ☐ Stretching or exercising

What are your favorite and most accessible self-care activities?

_____

_____

_____

_____

15

Summary and Commitments for Your Scribe

Remember these key practices as you strengthen your Scribe.

- Use a daily writing practice as regular strength-training for the Scribe.
- Time to write doesn't just appear—you need to make it happen.
- Categorize writing as one of the important tasks in your life.
- Reinforce your plans with deadlines and accountability.
- Don't beat yourself up for doing less than you hoped.

My Commitments to My Scribe

_____

_____

_____

_____

PART FOUR

Find Flow

Have you ever lost track of time when you're engaged in writing or other creative work? You look up and realize that it's dinner time or you're late to a meeting. You were completely wrapped up in the work and time just flew. You were immersed in the state of *flow*.

When you can reach a state of flow while writing, it elevates the entire experience. If flow is part of your writing life, it's easier to stay motivated, build your skills, and persist through difficult times.

The best, most durable writing practices encourage a state of flow. But before building it into the writing process, you must understand how it works, in general and for you.

In this part, you'll dig deeper into what flow looks like in your life—writing and otherwise.

16

Nine Attributes of Flow

In his excellent book *Flow: The Psychology of Optimal Experience*, the psychologist Mihaly Csikszentmihalyi identified flow as a state having the following nine attributes.

1. Challenging work that is within your abilities
2. Clear goals for the work (you know what you need to do)
3. Immediate feedback through the activity itself
4. A complete focus on the action
5. The absence of distractions or mind wandering
6. No fear of failure
7. Lack of self-consciousness
8. The loss of awareness of time passing
9. An overall sense of fulfillment or enjoyment

The list looks long, but from the writer's perspective, these attributes could be contained in three buckets:

1. The work
2. The environment
3. Your mindset

The following exercises will help you understand how to manage those three variables in a way to increase the frequency of flow in your writing life. First, though, let's look at what it feels like for you.

17

Identify Flow When It Happens

Do you experience flow in your life?

Flow-inducing experiences can include physical activities (like sports), hobbies (playing an instrument, making pottery), playing games, even really digging into a spreadsheet if you're a numbers person.

Note: Flow is an active state, not a passive one. A movie may be engrossing, but watching it isn't the same thing as entering a state of flow. Flow comes from your mental state engaging in a challenging task.

When's the last time you've achieved a state of flow in any activity, writing or otherwise? (Don't feel bad if you don't remember achieving flow—the exercises that follow should help with that.)

_____

_____

_____

_____

What did it feel like? What do you remember from this?

_____

_____

_____

_____

What was different about it from your writing?

_____

_____

_____

_____

The irony of identifying flow in your life is that you can only spot it *after* it's happened. (Self-awareness is the enemy of flow.)

Try keeping a flow journal for a while, to see when you experience flow, what you were doing, and about how long it lasted. Keep this going until it has happened several times. Every time you enter a state of flow, make a note of it. Patterns should start to appear over time.

The Flow Journal

DATE	FLOW EXPERIENCE OBSERVATIONS
	• What I was doing • How long it lasted • Other notes
	• What I was doing • How long it lasted • Other notes
	• What I was doing • How long it lasted • Other notes
	• What I was doing • How long it lasted • Other notes
	• What I was doing • How long it lasted • Other notes

18

Flow-Friendly Work

Finding flow is partly about matching the task at hand to your writing skills. The work must be challenging enough to be engaging, but also within your abilities.

The best way to do this is to break your work into smaller components and tackle each one separately.

Writing a book is a tall order. But you can dive into writing 750 words on one small section of the book and accomplish it in one sitting.

Even if you're writing something much smaller than a book—say, a blog post—you can always break it down into manageable components.

Experiment with taking this approach in your writing life. Pick a project. Choose a section of the story or a chapter of a nonfiction book. Then break it into as many components as you can.

Experiment with finding smaller tasks to work on. Then, use the practices on the following pages to see if you can enter a state of flow when working on any part of the process.

Flow-Friendly Project Worksheet

PROJECT:
The first thing I need to do is:
Here's another task in the project:
Another task:
Another task:
Another task:
Another task:

19

Manage the Environment

Create a writing environment where you can put your complete focus on the work (see #4 of the 9 attributes on page 57), without any distractions (see #5).

Some authors retreat to Instagram-worthy writing spaces or check into a cabin in the woods. Most of us don't have that luxury, nor do we need it.

Instead, we need separation from the distractions and interruptions of the world. This distance can be fleeting and minor. Here are a few strategies that work for writers.

Shut Down Interruptions

How can you reduce interruptions from the outside world? Select the techniques that work for you when you're chasing flow:

- ☐ Closing the door
- ☐ Turning off Wi-Fi (drastic, I know)
- ☐ Silencing notifications on phones and computers
- ☐ Writing with pencil and paper, away from computers
- ☐ Writing on a separate laptop
- ☐ Using distraction-free writing apps
- ☐ Hanging a "Do Not Disturb" sign or wearing a special hat to signal to those around you that you don't welcome interruptions
- ☐ Other [Fill in your favorite]:

_____

_____

Dedicate a Special Time

Many people write first thing in the day. I often do too, because otherwise I get pulled into tasks for other people.

What's your best time to write?

_____

_____

Set the Soundscape

Even if you cannot create a perfect writing studio, you can control the soundscape. Research has shown that sound affects our focus and creativity.

Most writers I know have a preferred background noise. What's your favorite?

- ☐ Complete silence
- ☐ White noise
- ☐ Music—*your favorite type*: _____
- ☐ Distant conversation
- ☐ Traffic or urban sounds
- ☐ Birdsong
- ☐ Other:

_____

_____

See what works for you as an environment for flow. Technology can help. If you need silence or white noise, consider noise-cancelling headphones. Look into the many phone or computer apps that offer creativity playlists, white noise, or more.

An app called Coffitivity replicates the sound of a coffee shop for those who love writing in coffee shops but cannot always get to one.

You may find that you prefer different types of sound for different tasks. For example, I find birdsong soothing while editing.

These practices address the external environment. The toughest hurdles often live within us.

20

Mental Systems and Mindset

Just a second, I'm going to check my social media...

We like to blame new technologies for our inability to find flow. But the world has long trained us to distract ourselves. Much of the blame lies within us. We are social beings, constantly pulled to what other people are doing.

Review attributes 5–8 on the Flow list:

- The absence of distractions or mind wandering
- No fear of failure
- Lack of self-consciousness
- The loss of awareness of time passing

These all take place within *you*. If you want to write in a state of flow, you'll need to do inner housekeeping.

Banish Multitasking

Science demonstrates that you lose valuable momentum every time you switch between tasks, even if you *think* you're a multitasking whiz.

Don't try to squeeze anything else into your writing time, even if it would only take a moment to do. If you think of something you must do, write it down on a list and return to your writing.

Put Fear Aside

If you've broken the work into small enough chunks, give yourself permission to simply work on this next step without worrying about what will happen when you're done. If the inner critic starts chiming in, kindly tell it to wait for its turn, in revision. Then get back to writing.

Let a Machine Manage the Time

Set a timer for a period of time long enough to for you to become immersed in the work. Perhaps you work well in 25-minute sprints or 45-minute blocks.

Using a timer achieves two things:

1. It prevents you from watching the clock and being aware of time passing (pulling yourself out of a flow state).
2. It offers a useful way to handle distracting thoughts and ideas. When you think of a task you need to do, tell yourself, "I'll do it once the timer goes off. This is my writing time."

What Keeps You from Flow?

The next time you're writing, notice the other things that you do. Here are several common writing distractions. Do you do any of them?

- ☐ Checking email
- ☐ Reading all those emails you subscribe to
- ☐ The Google/YouTube search rabbit hole
- ☐ Social media
- ☐ Cleaning the house (not *my* main distraction)
- ☐ Texting friends
- ☐ News

Recognize your go-to habits, and you'll know how to protect yourself from them.

Other Things I Do When I Am Writing

_____

_____

21

Find Fluidity with Freewriting

Attribute #7 of flow is "lack of self-consciousness." For many people, writing without judgment, criticism, and self-consciousness takes practice.

Perhaps you hear the voice of a childhood teacher criticizing your writing. Or maybe you feel compelled to transform your thoughts into a more "writerly" form and that slows you down.

If you want greater fluidity connecting the ideas in your head, you may have to practice getting out of your own way. The best way to do that is freewriting—writing quickly and fluidly, without judgment, for the sake of going fast.

Freewriting trains your Muse and Scribe to work together toward a common goal. It's like a practice session for achieving the state of flow. Make it part of your writing life, or experiment with it until you feel more fluid with writing.

Basic Freewriting

Get your writing gear together. You can type or write by hand—you might experiment with both.

1. *Choose a goal.* Pick either a time or word/page count. Start small until you're accustomed to it. For example, plan to write for 10 minutes or 300 words.
2. *Choose a topic.* The topic can shift and change. If nothing else, write about your plans for the day or your writing dreams.
3. *Set a timer* (if you're using time) and start writing. Don't judge. Don't correct grammar or spelling or stop to evaluate what you've done. Just keep writing. If your brain sputters to a stop, prompt it. Keep writing, even if it's filler like: "I've run out of things to say, I wonder what my friend Jo would say about this situation?" Just keep writing.
4. *Stop* only when the timer rings or you've reached your word count.

Use a journal, an online file, or simply fill the next page.

Once you're done, congrats! You've practiced fluid writing.

If you found it too difficult, try The Most Dangerous Writing App (MDWA). It creates an environment where, if you pause for 5 seconds, your work is wiped out. Find the link in the resources for this book at AnneJanzer.com/Resources.

Freewriting

Fill this page by writing fluidly, without stopping. No one needs to see it.

_____

_____

_____

_____

_____

_____

_____

_____

_____

_____

_____

_____

_____

_____

_____

_____

_____

_____

_____

_____

_____

22

Summary and Commitments for Flow

Flow happens when a magical combination of things occurs. The work is challenging but possible. You focus completely on it, without distractions, fear, and self-consciousness. You cannot *force* yourself into a state of flow, but you can attract it by meeting its requirements.

Manage the work: Break the work into achievable but challenging chunks.

Create a flow-friendly environment: Set the stage by eliminating distractions and interruptions. Silence your notifications. Use sound apps to create the sonic environment.

Mange the mindset: Minimize the temptations of multitasking and self-distraction. Use a timer if that helps.

Find fluidity: Try freewriting to practice drafting without self-consciousness and judgment.

Commitments to Optimizing Flow

I resolve to do the following to protect or expand the amount of time I spend writing in flow.

1. _____

2. _____

3. _____

PART FIVE

YOUR WRITING RECIPE

Writing is like baking yeast bread. You can't rush through the recipe all at once and produce anything edible. You need to give the yeast enough time and the right environment to do its magic.

Proficient bakers know how to work with the yeast, the ambient temperature, and the other conditions to produce consistent results. You can find and follow a recipe to make a yeasted or sourdough bread, but experience teaches you what works in your kitchen. Mastery comes through doing, not reading.

With that in mind, here's a basic writing recipe. It's a starting point.

Try it out, then come up with your own favorite ways to put the steps together. Figure out what works for you, then learn to trust your recipe.

23

The Basic Recipe

This is a basic recipe for writing, applicable for many situations and projects. Try it out.

1. **Research**. Gather the ingredients through research (freewriting and external research). You may continue researching even as you write.
2. **Incubate**. Leave time to activate the Muse before you start drafting. Your brain is like the yeast organisms in bread dough, breathing life into the raw materials you've accumulated. Give it a chance to work.
3. **Structure**. Read your notes and decide on the structure of your piece (outline, mind map, storyboard, etc.).
4. **Assemble**. Get the first draft down on paper. It can be ugly and imperfect—that's fine. Trust your process. You'll fix it.
5. **Let it rest**. Just as you would leave the bread dough alone to rise, let the first draft sit so you can get distance. Thoughts, phrases, different perspectives, and inspiration often strike as the draft rests.
6. **Revise and proof**. Wrestle with the piece from different angles, shaping it into its final form.
7. **Publish**. Decide when it's ready to put in front of readers. Impatient as you may be for the final product, you don't want to put your work out in the world half-baked.

Do You Skip Any of Those Steps?

Does that recipe surprise you? Do you usually try to start at step 4, drafting?

Check any of the steps that you may skip and ask yourself if your writing suffers because of it.

- ☐ Research
- ☐ Incubate
- ☐ Structure
- ☐ Assemble
- ☐ Let it rest
- ☐ Revise and proof
- ☐ Publish

Recipe Variations

You might have different approaches for various types of writing. A book or a poem, for example, may require more iterative cycles than a blog post. Perhaps you prefer to layer incubation at nearly every phase of the writing.

You don't have to be neat, or perfect, or follow these steps.

Your challenge: Add your preferences and best processes to the recipe to make it your own. Use the work you did in the sections on the Muse, the Scribe, and Flow, and work through the recipe sections that follow to see how they match.

Your goal: Come up with a repeatable process *that you trust*, that carries you through the writing as efficiently and easily as possible.

Let's get cooking.

24

Gather the Ingredients with Research

Most writing, even fiction and memoir, begins with research. Much of the research is internal:

- Thinking about the reader and what they need
- Surveying what you know about a topic
- Envisioning the piece you want to write

Internal research may lead you to identify external sources to support the project:

- Interviewing people who are part of a memoir
- Researching settings and professions for a story
- Finding studies and statistics to support your point in nonfiction

My own survey of nonfiction authors shows that most continue researching after they start writing. (See the book *Get the Word Out* for more insights on writing a nonfiction book.)

Don't worry about completing the research step. Set out on this phase as early as you can to get the Muse interested in the topic.

Recipe:
Research

Who's in Charge: The Scribe

Ingredients

- Focused attention for reading and note-taking
- Periods of open attention to look for connections and avenues of research
- Interviews, books, online sources
- Pen/paper or word processor for freewriting
- Tools for taking notes and organizing results (Evernote, Scrivener, etc.)

Steps

1. Gather the research or conduct interviews.
2. Freewrite to explore.
3. Consolidate and review your notes.

The Research Plan

Make a short research plan for your writing project.

Inner Research

Options include freewriting, talking with others, drawing, journaling, etc.

My *inner* research plan:

_____

_____

Start date:

_____

How long it should take:

_____

_____

Outer Research

My *outer* research plan:

_____

_____

Start date:

_____

How long it should take:

_____

_____

25

Let It Rise: Incubation

Incubation (or letting ideas simmer with your Muse) happens repeatedly in the writing process—before or after outlining, during the drafting, or before revision.

Don't try to incubate at the very start of a project. The Muse needs something to work with, whether you've gotten there through research, writing, or some combination of the two.

Return to your summary of the Muse methods at the end of Part Two, where you identified your most reliable places and activities for inspiration. Incubation happens there.

Make them part of your writing process.

Recipe:
Incubation

Who's in Charge: The Muse

Ingredients
- Open attention and solitude
- A break in time, and distance
- A piece of paper and pencil, or note-taking technology (in case sudden brilliance strikes)

Steps
1. Review the notes. Focus on one or two unresolved issues.
2. Step away from the work and do other things.
3. Take note of any insights that might arise.

My Regular Incubation Activities
Revisit the exercises in Part Two on finding open attention...

1. _____

2. _____

3. _____

26

Structure the Work

Before starting the draft, create a structure for the work.

It doesn't have to be a traditional outline. Experiment with your favorite ways to organize your thoughts. If you find them boring, try a different approach. You'll find options below.

Having a map before you set out gives the Scribe something to work with when planning the drafting.

Recipe: Structure

Who's in Charge: The Scribe

Ingredients

- Focused attention
- Notes from the research phase
- Your favorite outlining tools: pen or pencil and paper, word processor, mind-mapping software, note cards and markers, whiteboard, etc.

Steps

1. Clarify your objectives.
2. Review your research and notes.
3. Create the structure.
4. Paste your notes into the outline structure to prime the drafting.

Outlining Methods

Your writing structure doesn't have to look like a traditional outline.

For example, mind mapping is the process of writing down themes or ideas and then drawing out related ideas and making connections between them. You can find explanations and software online. Because it traces nonlinear thoughts, mind mapping invites the Muse's associative thought processes into the act of creating a structure.

If you like to think tactically, consider collecting ideas and concepts on note cards, then sorting and organizing them.

You might also create a storyboard of your project—aligning concepts or images much like a screenwriter plotting out a movie. (This works well for visual thinkers.)

Choose the methods that work for you:

☐ Traditional outline
☐ Mind map
☐ Storyboard
☐ Note cards
☐ Other:

_____

_____

Warning: Beware of spending so much time learning a new outline tool or process that you don't think about the writing.

27

Work the Dough: Write the Draft

Getting the first draft down on paper is the heart of the process. This is when the Muse and the Scribe work together.

Drafting is most rewarding when you experience a sense of flow. Revisit the ideas you noticed for setting up your environment for flow.

- *Project scope*: Choose an immediate task with an identifiable goal (for example, 500 words of your next chapter).
- *Environment*: Choose the physical (and sonic) environment that suits you best.
- *Mindset*: Create the single-minded focus you need for writing. One writer friend of mine faithfully listened to upbeat music every morning because he knew that creativity required a positive mindset.

When you commit to writing fluidly, you will inevitably leave holes or gaps in the manuscript or skim over a concept that needs detail. You may need to make an extra layering pass part of your drafting process, to complete the rough draft.

Recipe
Drafting

Who's in Charge: The Scribe and the Muse collaborate (when you realize flow) or contribute in alternating bursts (the rest of the time)

Ingredients
- Periods of both focused and open attention
- A distraction-free place to work (your ideal environment for flow)
- Your favorite tools for drafting

Steps
1. Define your objectives.
2. Write without self-criticism.
3. Rest.
4. Revisit, add a layer, and continue.

Work on the Easiest Part First

Just because a reader may travel from start to finish doesn't mean you have to write that way.

Write the bits that feel ready to write, even if they're out of order. Because when you feel ready to work on something, your Muse is interested. The writing will be easier.

You can assemble everything and fix the flow in the revision process.

Think of your current writing project. What seems like it would be easy or fun to write? That's what you should do first. (The work may lead you in a different direction. That's interesting, too.)

What do you feel ready to write today? Right now?

_____

_____

_____

_____

The Layering Pass

Just as bread doughs may require two cycles of kneading and rising, a draft may take more than one pass before it's ready for the next step of revision.

The writing teacher Donald Murray taught the idea of *layering*—taking a second pass through the first draft to add another layer of detail or texture. Many writers do this. It often takes more than one pass to come up with a true "first" draft.

Use this opportunity to complete and improve the draft:

- Adding detail
- Cutting unnecessary information
- Filling in transitions and gaps you may have left while drafting fluidly

If you commit to making one layering pass before you consider the first draft complete, you'll find revision much more enjoyable.

This commitment also helps in the initial drafting process, since it means that you can leave notes to yourself like [*fix this*] or [*write a transition here*] and keep moving quickly.

28

Let It Rest

Once you've finished the rough draft, take a break. You've earned it. Perhaps reward yourself with an activity that replenishes you.

Recipe
Resting

Who's in Charge: The Scribe *must* take a break during this phase; the Muse may choose to return

What You Need
- At least one full night of sleep
- Elapsed time

Steps
1. Let time pass.

What are your favorite self-care and replenishing activities? Find the ones that give you energy or restore you when you're drained. Here are a few ideas.

☐ Being in nature
☐ Exercising
☐ Spending time with friends
☐ Spending time with a good book

My Favorite Replenishing Activities

_____

_____

_____

_____

29

Make It Wonderful: Revise

Revising is the least appreciated part of writing. Yet it's the difference between adequate and special. Great writing emerges from revision.

The key with revision is, of course, to have a process. The longer the work, the more important process becomes. You can easily get lost revising.

Make a plan and work through it.

1. Schedule time in advance for revising.
2. Decide how many revision passes you will take.
3. Track your progress and don't skip steps.

Recipe
Revision

Who's in Charge: The Scribe runs this phase, ideally with occasional input from the Muse

What You Need
- Focused attention
- The rough draft
- Editing tools (paper, electronic)
- Friends, editors, colleagues
- Patience

Steps

1. Start with structure and work your way down.
2. Revise tone and style for reader's flow.
3. Copyedit and look for your personal, targeted list of writing mannerisms. (See the section Your Personal Search List, below.)
4. Proofread.

Enlist outside help for any or all of these steps.

The Telescoping Revision Plan

To be as efficient as possible, always work from the widest lens to the most specific when revising.

1. Start with the big picture. Does the piece meet your objectives and the reader's needs? Is the content in the right order, and is anything missing?
2. Next, revise for flow. Will the reader get stuck and have to double back to make sense of a sentence or paragraph? Is the tone right for the audience? Can you make it livelier or more authoritative?
3. Polish and improve. Look for tired metaphors, repeated words, dull adjectives. Pick stronger verbs. Tighten and clarify.
4. Format and proofread.

Getting the order right is important. Otherwise, you might spend hours polishing words that need to be cut or changed.

To make sure you follow the plan, create a checklist. The actual tasks will vary based on the kind of thing you're writing.

Revision Checklist

First Pass: Big Picture

- ☐ The content meets my overall objectives.
- ☐ The content serves the reader's needs.
- ☐ It's in the right order.
- ☐ Nothing important is missing.

Second Pass: Flow

- ☐ It reads well from start to finish.
- ☐ The reader won't get lost in complex sentences.
- ☐ The overall tone is right for the audience and content.

Third Pass: Copyedit and Polish

Check for the following:

- ☐ Overused or inappropriate metaphors
- ☐ Repetitive words
- ☐ Tired or boring verbs
- ☐ Your personal search list (see the next section)

When you've done this, run it through spelling and grammar checking software and decide which issues to fix. You don't have to accept all of the recommendations, but you should understand why they happened.

Fourth Pass: Proofreading

Once the piece is in its final layout, check it one more time for formatting issues, typos, and other glitches.

Your Personal Search List

We each have our own writing mannerisms that are hard for us to see. Which of the following crop up in your first drafts?

☐ Excessive use of the passive voice (too much is boring)
☐ Boring verbs, especially the overuse of "is"
☐ Excessive use of abstractions (*there is* and *it is*)
☐ Snoozer adjectives: Big, little, good, bad
☐ Weakening words: Very, really, kind of, sort of, some
☐ Clichés

If you spot these in your work, don't beat yourself up. They're common and normal. Don't attempt to fix them when you're drafting because they're part of how you think.

Instead, hunt them down during that third revision pass. Before that, you need to know what they are. Here are a few ways to build your own target list.

- Run the copy through software like Grammarly, ProWritingAid, WordRake, or anything else that looks at style and structure. Notice the repeated recommendations and look for trends that you want to change.
- Hire a copyeditor or get a friend with a copyediting eye to edit your work. Invite them to comment on the issues that pop up most often.
- Read your writing aloud and notice anything awkward or words and phrases you find yourself saying frequently.

List the top three things you want to search for in your writing. For example, your list might have three buckets:

1. Weakening words and phrases
2. Overuse of abstractions
3. Snoozer adjectives

Changing even 20 percent of personal tics and habitual patterns will make your writing stronger.

My Personal Target List

1. _____

2. _____

3. _____

Refer to this list during revision.

Over time, you may discover that your top three items change. That's usually a sign of progress.

Proofreading

For important work like a book, hire a professional proofreader. For smaller or less critical projects, get other people to look at your work.

It's nearly impossible to proofread your own work accurately. If you must, here are a few strategies to try:

- *Give yourself time.* Let it rest at least overnight, to get distance so you can see typos and missing words.
- *Use software* but proofread again after it runs. Software may introduce its own errors and cannot catch many glitches.
- *Change the format.* If you were revising online, print the piece to proof it. If you were working on paper, even changing the font can help.
- *Read it aloud.* This is the gold standard. Read the piece as if you were recording it. (Or make a recording—adding audio to print is a wonderful practice.) When you force yourself to slow down and read each word, you find many errors.

Finally, know that typos and problems happen—no one is immune. Treat searching for problems like a treasure hunt rather than a trial.

30

Serve It Up: Publish

Sometimes, the hardest part of writing is putting the work into the world. Fear and self-doubt creep in. It's easier to keep revising or to postpone the work indefinitely.

When the work is ready to publish (or your deadline is upon you), take action.

This section includes a few tips that may help you with this step.

Recipe
Publishing

Who's in Charge: The Scribe

Ingredients
- A deadline (external or internal)
- Due diligence plan

Steps
1. Let the draft sit at least overnight.
2. Decide to publish.

Define Your Due Diligence

Q: When do I publish?
A: When it's good enough for the reader.
Q: How do I know?
A: Do your due diligence.

In legal discussions, *due diligence* refers to taking "reasonable care" to protect against accident or harm, or to ensure a sound decision.

Your standard of due diligence will depend on many factors:

- *Your personal preferences and abilities.* The farther you go in your career, the more exacting your standard may become.
- *The project and subject.* A personal blog post probably needs less fact checking and diligence than textbooks or medical advice.
- *The reader.* Are you writing for a discerning reader who is going to luxuriate in your word choices? For someone seeking entertainment or education? What do they need from your work? Find out and make sure you can deliver.

Put aside a few moments to create a due diligence plan for publishing the piece.

Factors may include:

- Other eyes: Will you hire a book coach or developmental editor (someone who helps you with structure)? Find early readers in your area?
- How many revision passes will you take? See the Revision Checklist on page 93.
- Fact checking: Will you hire a pro? Do it yourself?
- Copyediting: Can you hire a professional? Get other experienced copyeditors to help? Use software?
- Layout and design: What does the project require?
- Proofreading: Will you hire a professional proofreader? Enlist your community?

Due Diligence Plan

Use this template to create a due diligence plan for your project. Whenever you feel fear or perfectionism raise its head, or if you're afraid to press Send or Publish, point at this piece of paper and reassure yourself that you've got this covered.

My Due Diligence Plan for _____

1. _____

2. _____

3. _____

4. _____

5. _____

6. _____

31

Your Personal Recipe

Now that you've used the basic recipe, how does it work for you?

Will you use it on your next project, or would you change it for your own style and personality?

For example, poets might want more incubation periods during drafting and revision, while nonfiction authors might add more research after outlining or starting the draft.

Make the recipe your own, using these basic steps:

Research

Incubation

Structure

Drafting

Resting

Revising

Publishing

Return to your notes from each section and use them to create your personal recipe card. Then post it somewhere to remind you to embrace and honor your process.

My Writing Recipe

Step 1:

Step 2:

Step 3:

Step 4:

Step 5:

Step 6:

Step 7:

Epilogue

Congratulations! You've done the hard work of identifying and refining your process. You've created your unique writing recipe.

If you've filled the pages and want to do more, find blank versions of the forms in this book on my website, at AnneJanzer.com/Resources. Use them if they help you refine your practices.

Remember the quadrant of the Muse and Scribe balance? By working through these pages, you've identified the ways to bring these into balance for your own work. You have the tools to spend more time in Creative Productivity, and less in Diligent Drudgery, Creative Chaos, or Uninspired Inertia.

Successful and productive writers have a strong sense of their own process. Now you have yours.

Go forth and write!

Made in the USA
Middletown, DE
09 March 2023

26496290R00064